Kavan Doherty	Donna Marie Mongan	Lily McGinley	Martine McSorely
Rachael Cawley	Shannon Cawley	Annie Stokes	Mary Harbinson Dermot
Micheal Connors	Josephine Doherty	Tom Christopher Ward	Madine Barry Coulter
Annie Doherty	Daniel Dundon	Margaret Rose Cawley	Una Herdman
John Doherty	Deliela Dundon	Martin Nolan Collins	Damien Fryers
Margaret Dundon	Rebecca Dundon	Shannon Doherty	Jane O'Hagan
Terence Heaney	Edward Gavin	Christina Heaney	Kevin Connolly
Francie Joyce	Peter Gavin	Darren Maughan	Joanne McFall
Paddy Kelly	Shannon Heaney	Donna Maughan.	Chris McClean
Helen Maughan	Annie Keenan	Nan McGinley	Maureen Cassidy
Shannon Maughan	Mary Kelly	Annie Mongan	Clare Walsh
Paddy McDonagh	Martin Maughan	Caroline Mongan	Anne Stewart
Brigid Mongan	Shannon Maughan	James Mongan	Rose Rooney
Naomi Mongan	Martin Gary McDonagh	Thomas Mongan	Paddy Copeland
Tom Mongan	Annalise Mongan	Brian Gavin	Gina Johnson
Winnie Marie Mongan	Jacqueline Mongan	Patrick Joyce.	Marie Shannon
Martin Stokes	John Mongan	Anthony Maughan	Anne McGuigan
Nan Connors	William Mongan	Melissa Maughan	Liz Weir
Hughie Doherty	Louise Ward	Nan McDonagh	Mags Dundon
Jonny Doherty	Martin Cawley	Jack McGinley	Kathleen Connors
Santana Dundon	John Connors	Melissa Mongan	Fiona Lovely
Edward Keenan	Rebecca Doherty	Patrick Gerard Mongan	Lucy Oman
Andrew Maughan	Christopher Heaney	Priscilla Mongan	Annemarie Connors
Martina Maughan	Barney Joyce	Gerry Murphy	Emer Maguire
Theresa McGinley	Kim Kelly	John McCaffrey	Orla Kenny
Biddy Mongan	Natasha Maughan	Sarah McVeigh	

LIVING IN A TRAILER

I like living in a trailer because we can travel anywhere we like. We travel to lots of different places because we can bring our trailer on the boat. We can visit our people and see our cousins in England. When we go to England we can settle in sunny Manchester.

Lily McGinley, age 8

I am a Traveller
I travel every day
I hate when we travel
On a sunny day

I am a Traveller
I go to school
I read and I write
It's very cool

Annie Mongan, age 10

Me father and mother would have spent a lot of time in the county Derry country and all around the county Antrim. You know they would have just travelled everywhere; there was no limits to the places where they would have went.

Mags Dundon, storyteller.

When my mummy was younger she used to live in a tent and she used to be afraid of the storm.

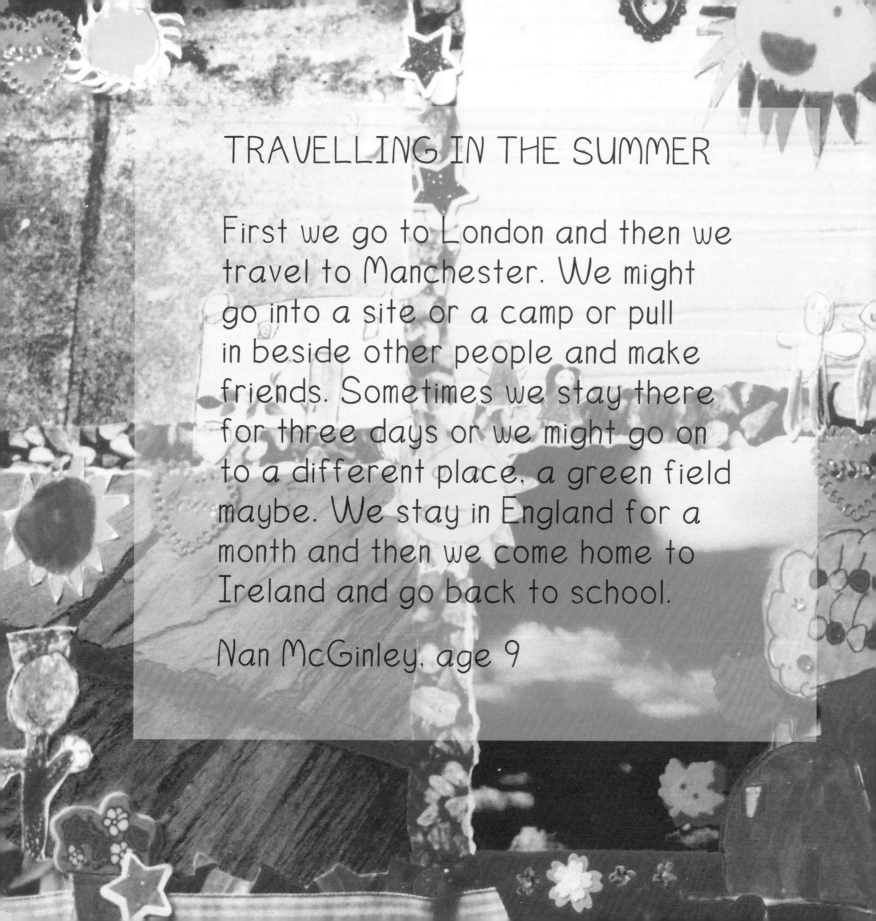

TRAVELLING IN THE SUMMER

First we go to London and then we travel to Manchester. We might go into a site or a camp or pull in beside other people and make friends. Sometimes we stay there for three days or we might go on to a different place, a green field maybe. We stay in England for a month and then we come home to Ireland and go back to school.

Nan McGinley, age 9

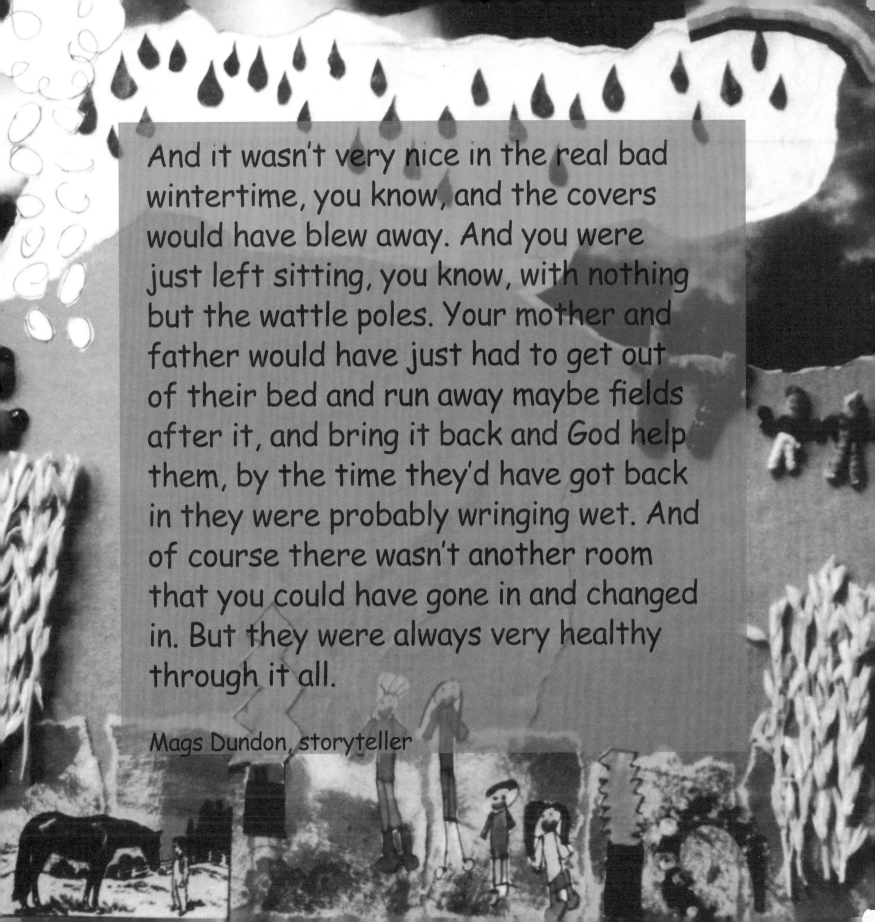

And it wasn't very nice in the real bad wintertime, you know, and the covers would have blew away. And you were just left sitting, you know, with nothing but the wattle poles. Your mother and father would have just had to get out of their bed and run away maybe fields after it, and bring it back and God help them, by the time they'd have got back in they were probably wringing wet. And of course there wasn't another room that you could have gone in and changed in. But they were always very healthy through it all.

Mags Dundon, storyteller

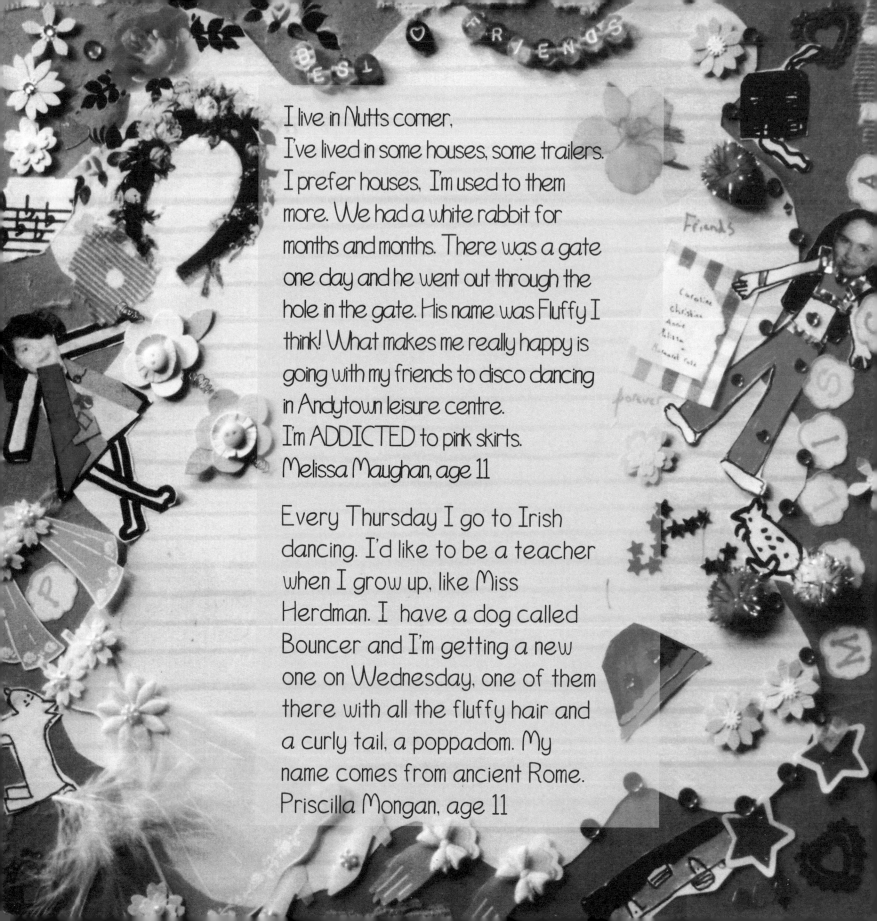

I live in Nutts corner,
I've lived in some houses, some trailers.
I prefer houses, I'm used to them
more. We had a white rabbit for
months and months. There was a gate
one day and he went out through the
hole in the gate. His name was Fluffy I
think! What makes me really happy is
going with my friends to disco dancing
in Andytown leisure centre.
I'm ADDICTED to pink skirts.
Melissa Maughan, age 11

Every Thursday I go to Irish
dancing. I'd like to be a teacher
when I grow up, like Miss
Herdman. I have a dog called
Bouncer and I'm getting a new
one on Wednesday, one of them
there with all the fluffy hair and
a curly tail, a poppadom. My
name comes from ancient Rome.
Priscilla Mongan, age 11

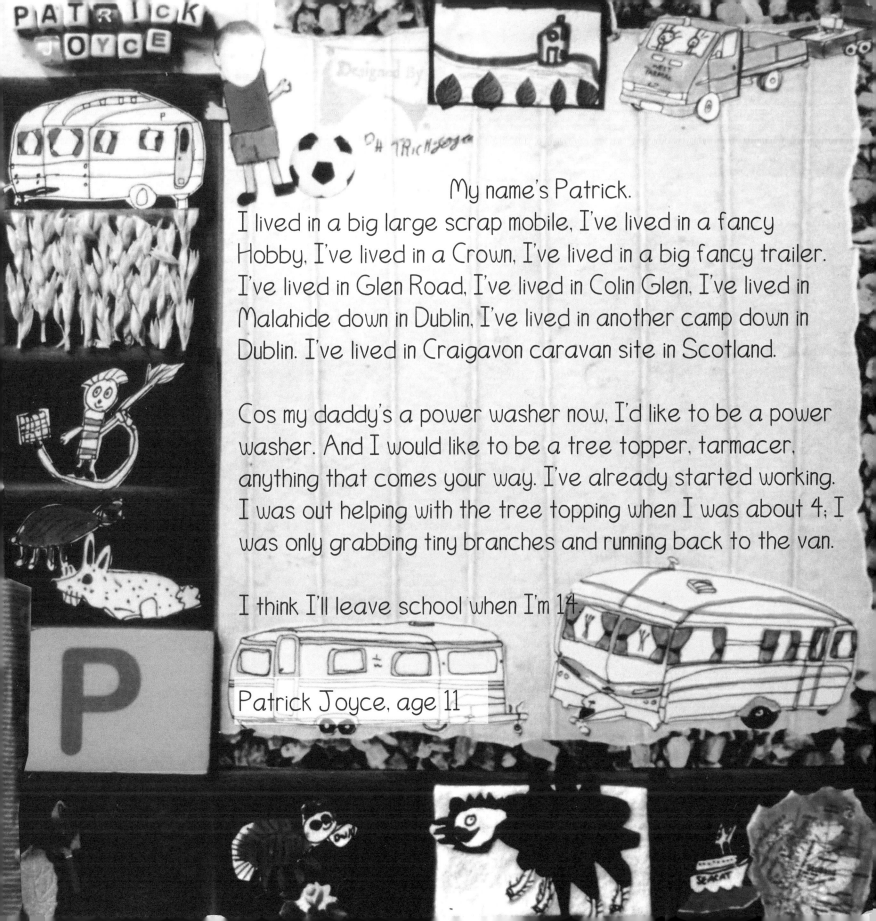

My name's Patrick.

I lived in a big large scrap mobile, I've lived in a fancy Hobby, I've lived in a Crown, I've lived in a big fancy trailer. I've lived in Glen Road, I've lived in Colin Glen, I've lived in Malahide down in Dublin, I've lived in another camp down in Dublin. I've lived in Craigavon caravan site in Scotland.

Cos my daddy's a power washer now, I'd like to be a power washer. And I would like to be a tree topper, tarmacer, anything that comes your way. I've already started working. I was out helping with the tree topping when I was about 4; I was only grabbing tiny branches and running back to the van.

I think I'll leave school when I'm 14.

Patrick Joyce, age 11

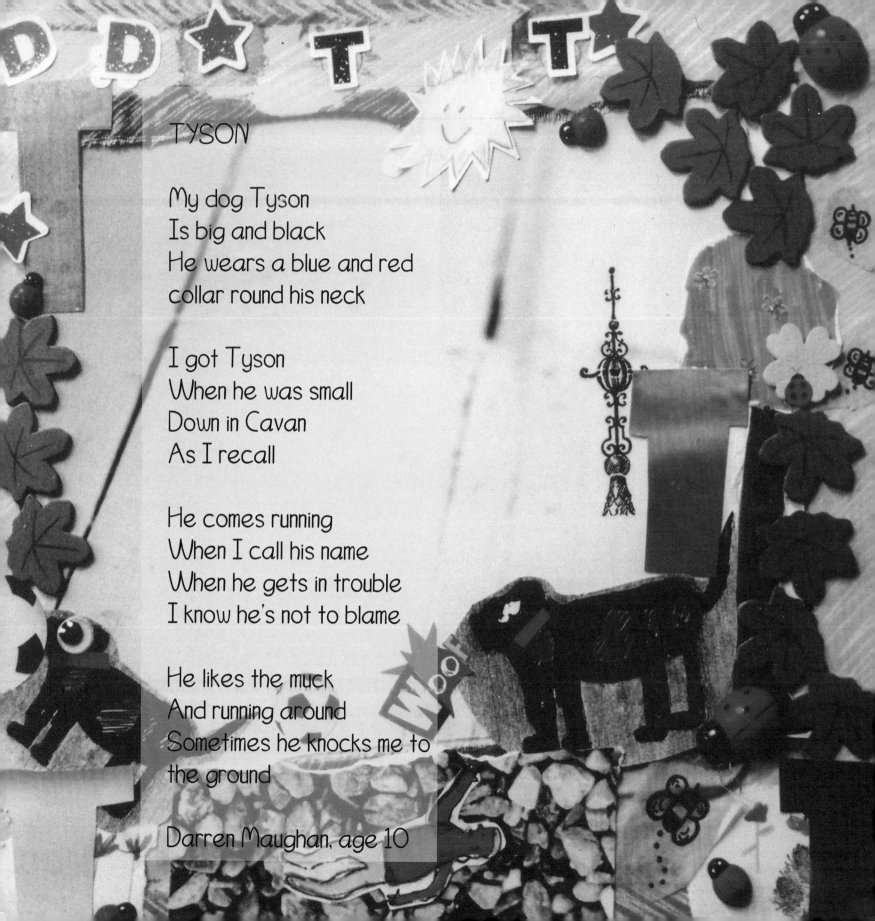

TYSON

My dog Tyson
Is big and black
He wears a blue and red
collar round his neck

I got Tyson
When he was small
Down in Cavan
As I recall

He comes running
When I call his name
When he gets in trouble
I know he's not to blame

He likes the muck
And running around
Sometimes he knocks me to
the ground

Darren Maughan, age 10

My granda has horses in the field. He keeps the horses for racing and trotting. He goes racing every month and he brings me with him. He has been racing since he was five years old. He gets his horse Lucky ready for the racing. He lives in Glengormley. He always wins a big trophy because he brings his best horse with him. My granda's daddy took him racing as well and he took my mummy racing. Other Travellers go to the races.

Delilah Dundon, age 7

I've got two favourite dogs and one is Tiny and one is Browny. One is brown and one is black and white. The little baby, Tiny, he always bites me.

Johnny Connors, age 9

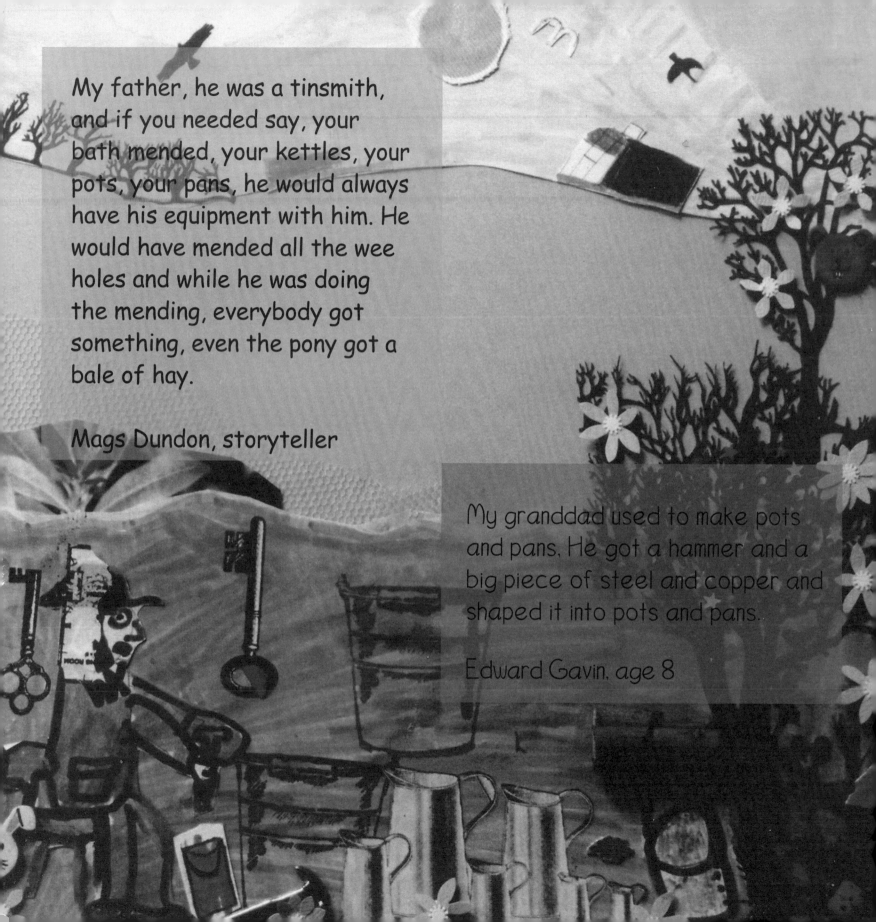

My father, he was a tinsmith, and if you needed say, your bath mended, your kettles, your pots, your pans, he would always have his equipment with him. He would have mended all the wee holes and while he was doing the mending, everybody got something, even the pony got a bale of hay.

Mags Dundon, storyteller

My granddad used to make pots and pans. He got a hammer and a big piece of steel and copper and shaped it into pots and pans.

Edward Gavin, age 8

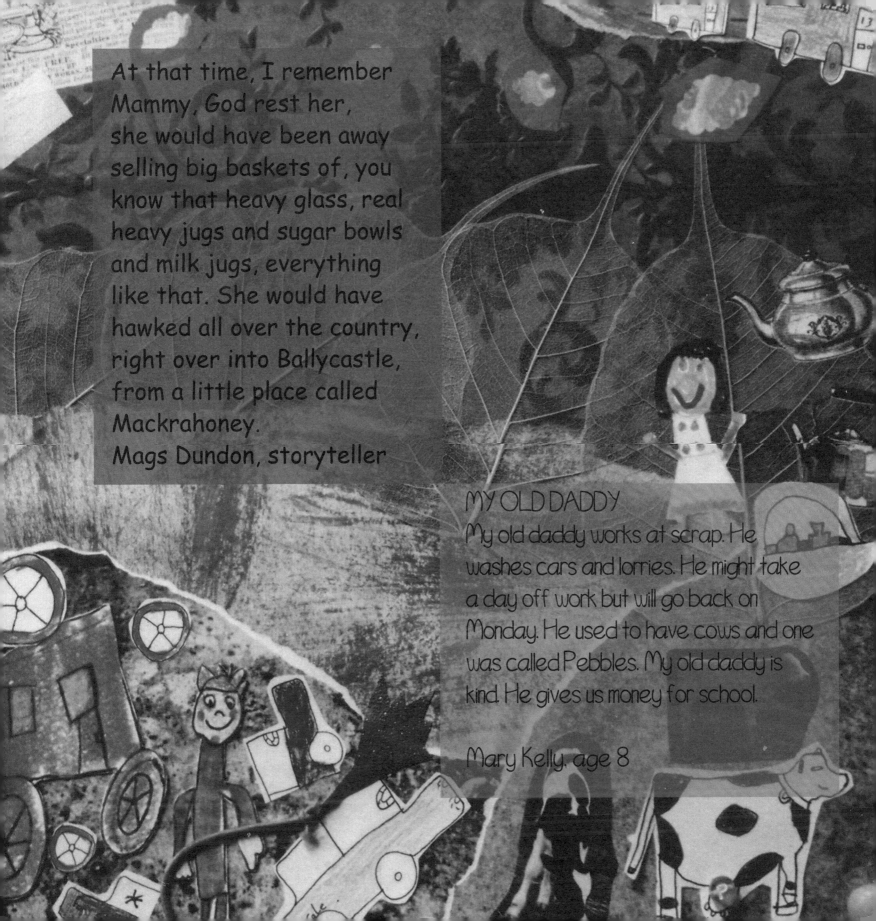

At that time, I remember Mammy, God rest her, she would have been away selling big baskets of, you know that heavy glass, real heavy jugs and sugar bowls and milk jugs, everything like that. She would have hawked all over the country, right over into Ballycastle, from a little place called Mackrahoney.

Mags Dundon, storyteller

MY OLD DADDY

My old daddy works at scrap. He washes cars and lorries. He might take a day off work but will go back on Monday. He used to have cows and one was called Pebbles. My old daddy is kind. He gives us money for school.

Mary Kelly, age 8

I brought him upstairs and gave him milk

I would wish for: to be rich, a square swimming pool, lovely jewellery.

Goldie was the first dog that never ran away or died in our family.

I like sunny days where the ground is all dry.

FRIENDS

Friends

The colour purple, it makes me smile.

Benches, basketball, dodge ball, baseball.

Going to the swimmers, disco dancing and Toy Master.

Our gang has a secret handshake.

Small mini pizzas.

Love

Margaret Rose Cawley, age 9.

Daniel Dundon

Rubber
hand roller
Spade
Shovel
bricks
cement

I go tarmacing with my Granddaddy. I have been going since I was one year old. We go to Lisburn and Glengormley and Toomebridge. I help roll the tarmac out on the road and hose the roller and the concrete. We do block paving. We spray the tarmac to clean it up and power wash the ground. We sand the block paving and put cement between the bricks. My granda has been doing this all his life. He started when he was a small boy just like me. The first time I ever done tarmacing I done it in Newtownards with my Daddy. I'm going to be a tarmac layer when I'm older.

Daniel Dundon, age 7

MY GRANNY HANNAH

My Granny and Granda used to shovel the snow for people when she was young for 50p. They used to buy sweets with the money. She also helped my Great Granda make pots and put them on the back of the wagon and sell them. My Great Granda hit the pots to shape them with rubber hammers and sold them to people.

Granny and Granda used to go fishing for food and mushrooms to put in the pot that Granda made.

Peter Gavin, age 6

Old cart

Lots of noise from the scrap
Dark nights. Everyone around
the camp. Nights are warm
around the fire. Dancing
around the fireside.
Altogether young and old,
Young at heart. Scrap and
carpets for sale.

John Mongan, age 8

Once upon a time an eagle was coming down and my cousin got a new pup, a terrier, and the eagle was coming down. But the eagle grabbed the pup and the eagle brought it up to the sky. But the eagle let it go and it came down and it died. It happened when I was over in England, when I was 10.

Jack McGinley, age 11.

I like living in a trailer because I have my own room and it is lovely. I go to see my sister over in England. England is better than Belfast.

Annie Stokes, age 9

The women always wore the aprons, yes it was like a pocket, a beady pocket. They would have made the fanciest of pockets which tied around them, and that was the only place to really carry important stuff that they wanted with them.

Mags Dundon, storyteller

BEADY POCKET

TRAILER
CARAVAN
HOUSE

We lived in a caravan.
We did not like it because
it was cold.. Now we live in
a house. Our days of the
caravan are over.

Barney Joyce, age 9

Travel,
Round,
A country,
Vans,
Everyone together,
Lonely fields,
Lanes at night,
Evening falls,
Reading to sleep,
Settle down

Edward Gavin, age 8

Policeman, policeman, Don't
arrest me, Arrest that man,
behind that tree. He stole
copper, I stole brass
Policeman, policeman
Kiss my a # #.

Patrick Gerard Mongan, age 11

I am a Traveller and I'm proud
to be, I live in a house beside
a tree. Some Travellers
caravans is on stone and muck,
I'm just glad mine is stuck.
When you live on a site
It does be noisy at night,
But when you live in a house
You can sleep to morning light.
On Travellers sites there
Might be mice, My house hasn't
because it's nice

Caroline Mongan, age 10
(my aunt Kathleen helped me with this)

We used a technique called COLLAGE to create the artwork in our book.

We tore, cut, drew, snipped, pasted, stuck, rubbed, peeled, and painted to make the artwork.

We hope you enjoy our book!!

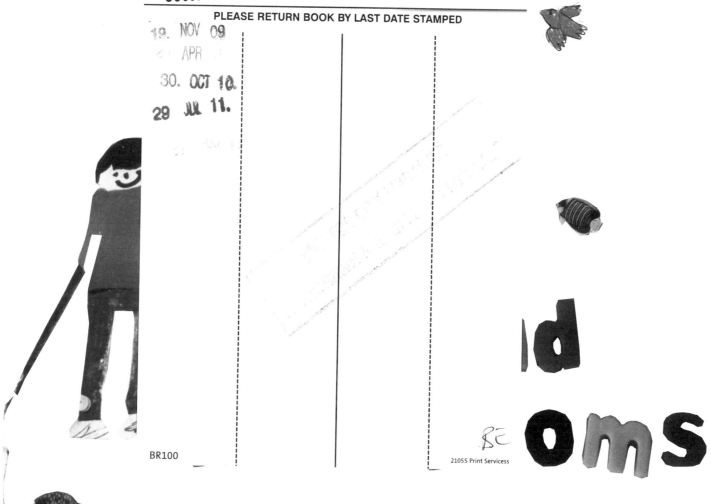

id

BE **oms**

 A KIDS' OWN BOOK

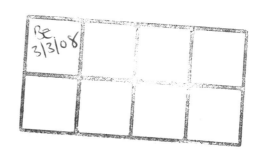

FISHING FOR FOOD AND MUSHROOMS is a collection of stories, poems and pen pictures written and illustrated by Traveller children in Belfast. The children worked with storytellers, artists, their teachers and families to discover more about the art and fun of storytelling and the important part it played in their history and cultural identity. The Gayla L'Esko Project (meaning 'Children's Stories') is a partnership arts and heritage education project between Belfast Traveller Support Group and St. Mary's Primary School, Divis St and Kids' Own Publishing Partnership. It was developed to engage Traveller children aged 4-12 years in celebrating their culture and history through the medium of language, storytelling, song and visual art.

This book is intended to make Traveller culture visible in schools and to provide fun reading material for any child.

This project and publication was made possible by the generous and imaginative support of The Heritage Lottery Fund.

Thanks, to all the young artists and adults who contributed to this book

Published By Kids' Own Publishing Partnership,
The Model Arts and Niland Gallery, The Mall, Sligo,
Republic of Ireland.
Tel: +353(0) 71 914 6364
Fax: +353(0) 71 914 6365
info@kidsown.ie
www.kidsown.ie